WOULD YOU RATHER

BOOK FOR KIDS

EVA BYRD

ISBN: 978-1-953149-04-6

Silly Jokes
& Fun Riddles

For Kids and Family

More bonus jokes, riddles and funny stories!

https://sendfox.com/lp/m58rrz

Introduction

We want to thank you for purchasing this book. This book is a collection of hilarious scenarios, wacky situations and tough choices for kids to have hours of fun with.

This is a neat tool to get a conversation started in an exciting and fun way. Don't forget to ask "Why" after a "Would you rather" question to get even more interesting answers and learn things about a person you didn't know before!

We know how important it is for children to learn, grow and read more; which is exactly why we wrote this book. Simple, fun and engaging games such as this book contains helps children become educated in a way that they even forget they're learning and developing valuable life skills.

So many more benefits:

DEVELOPS CRITICAL THINKING – Allows children to analyze and rationalize their choices. A sure way to help develop logical thinking skills for the rest of their lives.

ENCOURAGES COMMUNICATION – This book will help children interact, listen and feel comfortable reading aloud with others. It's an excellent way to connect. Not to mention, it's a fun way for parents to interact with their children and create unforgettable memories. If you're looking for a simple way to learn about your child's likes, dislikes and values, this is it!

BUILDS CONFIDENCE – While interacting with others, this can be a useful tool to help your children pronounce new vocabulary and even overcome shyness.

RULES OF THE GAME

NOTE: This game is best played with other people, so if you can, play it with friends and/or family.

Two players

- Player 1 takes the book and asks player 2 a question beginning with the phrase "Would you rather...?" Why...?
- After player 2 has made his/her choice, he or she will have to explain the reason why the choice was made.
- Pass the book to the other player, and they ask you a question.
- Have fun and don't forget to laugh a ton!

Three or four players

- Out of your group decide who will be the Question Master.
- The Question Master asks one question and "Why...?" from the book.
- The other players give their answers out loud.
- The Question Master decides who has given the best answer and gives one point to the winner. This is the answer with the best explanation for why.
- The answers can be funny, well thought out and even creative.
- The first player to reach 10 points wins!

LET'S HAVE SOME FUN!

WOULD YOU RATHER ...

own a fire-breathing dragon that will never hurt you

a dragon that breathes bubbles?

only eat pizza for the rest of your life

ice cream for the rest of your life?

WOULD YOU RATHER ...

be able to speak to animals

 OR

read people's minds?

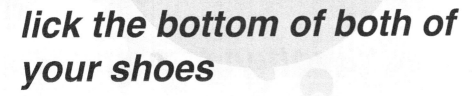

lick the bottom of both of your shoes

 OR

eat your boogers?

WOULD YOU RATHER ...

sneeze ricotta cheese

have chocolate tears?

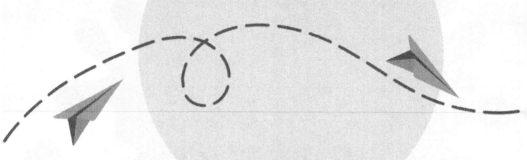

eat 3 rotten tomatoes

a can of old cat food?

WOULD YOU RATHER ...

discover a unicorn

find buried treasure?

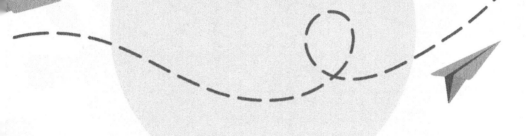

have the same name as your grandmother

have her same hairstyle?

WOULD YOU RATHER ...

always talk in rhyme

sing every time you speak?

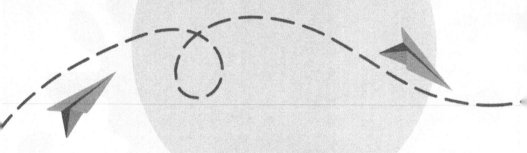

wear clown makeup every day for a year

wear a tutu for a year straight ?

WOULD YOU RATHER ...

hop around everywhere

OR

only be able to walk backwards?

have grass for armpit hair

OR

have a cucumber for a nose?

WOULD YOU RATHER ...

be able turn into a panda bear

OR

a kangaroo

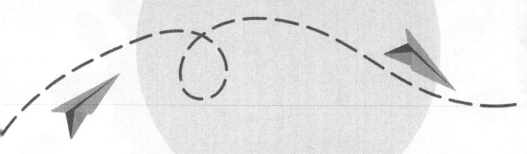

have hands instead of feet

OR

feet instead of hands?

WOULD YOU RATHER ...

have a cloak that makes you invisible

OR

have a magic wand to make things disappear?

find a magic lamp that gives you 2 wishes

OR

be able to breathe under water?

WOULD YOU RATHER ...

be able to walk up the side of tall buildings

OR

be able to jump right over them in a single bound?

take a nap with snakes

OR

kiss a jellyfish?

WOULD YOU RATHER ...

travel to the future and talk
to yourself for 10 minutes

OR

travel to the past and talk
to yourself for 20 minutes?

be the funniest

OR

the smartest person
alive?

WOULD YOU RATHER ...

be really good at water skiing

 **OR**

snowboarding?

be able to speak every language

 **OR**

have the ability to play every instrument?

WOULD YOU RATHER ...

visit a haunted castle

OR

stay in an underwater hotel?

live in a tree house

OR

a secret cave?

WOULD YOU RATHER ...

never use a phone again

OR

never watch tv again?

fly a spaceship to the moon

OR

or fly to Pluto?

WOULD YOU RATHER ...

be the best at painting

the best at dancing?

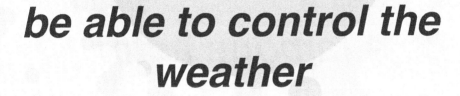

be able to control the weather

control people's minds?

WOULD YOU RATHER ...

have fingers for eyelashes

OR

tongues for fingers?

be a famous actor

OR

be a famous magician?

WOULD YOU RATHER ...

design a cool new toy

direct a best-selling movie?

be an extra in a really good movie

have a big part in a really bad movie?

WOULD YOU RATHER ...

always have a small rock in your shoes

OR

always have mud in your shoes?

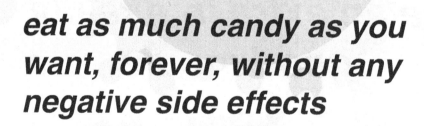

eat as much candy as you want, forever, without any negative side effects

OR

receive $1 million?

WOULD YOU RATHER ...

be forced to live the same day over and over again for a full year

OR

take 4 years off the end of your life?

always smell like garlic

OR

always smell like black pepper?

WOULD YOU RATHER ...

have a snowball fight with a penguin

OR

go swimming in Antarctica?

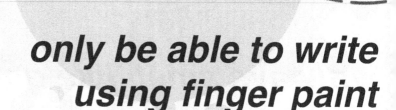

only be able to write using finger paint

OR

only be able to text while wearing mittens?

WOULD YOU RATHER ...

win an Olympic Gold Medal

OR

win an Academy Award?

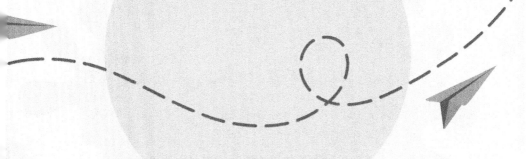

eat a spoonful of cinnamon

OR

eat a spoonful of horseradish?

WOULD YOU RATHER ...

be able to see through walls

OR

be able to do any math equation in your head?

have no elbows

OR

no knees?

WOULD YOU RATHER ...

be a wizard

OR

a superhero?

live in an amusement park

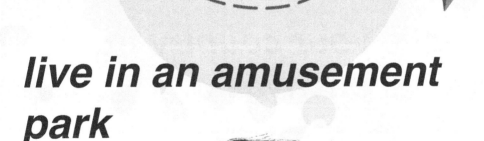
OR

in a zoo?

WOULD YOU RATHER ...

*never have homework
again*

OR

*be paid to do your
homework?*

**save your country from
an alien invasion**

OR

a terrible disease?

WOULD YOU RATHER ...

have the power to run as fast as the speed of light

OR

the power to walk through walls?

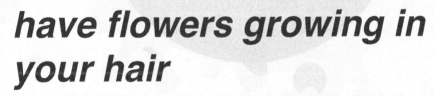

have flowers growing in your hair

OR

out of your belly button?

WOULD YOU RATHER ...

be able to type/text very fast

OR

be able to read very quickly?

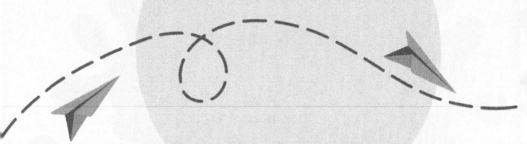

be able to control fire

OR

water?

WOULD YOU RATHER ...

invent a new holiday

OR

create a new sport?

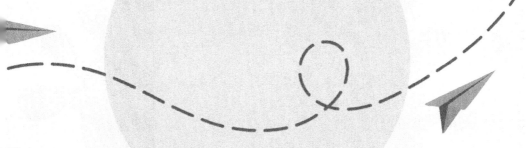

have ninja-like skills

OR

have the ability to fly?

WOULD YOU RATHER ...

swim in a pool of your favorite cereal and chocolate milk

OR

drink a cup of public pool water?

grow up with a pack wolves

OR

be raised by monkeys?

WOULD YOU RATHER ...

always travel by hot air balloon

OR

by riding in a kangaroo pouch?

have food magically appear anytime you want

OR

always know when someone is lying?

WOULD YOU RATHER ...

skip school for two months

OR

be able to make anyone laugh instantly for 2 months?

ride a friendly dragon

OR

a magical broomstick?

WOULD YOU RATHER ...

have super strength

OR

super speed?

be able to move things with your mind

OR

be able to teleport?

WOULD YOU RATHER ...

sleep in the North Pole every other night forever

OR

sleep in a giant freezer for 6 months straight?

only lip read for the rest of your life

OR

communicate through sign language?

WOULD YOU RATHER ...

be able to touch someone and make any pain go away

OR

touch any object and turn it into gold?

click your heels and your bedroom gets organized instantly

OR

snap your fingers and your lost items magically appear?

WOULD YOU RATHER ...

have hair that changes color with your mood

OR

skin that changes color with the temperature?

have a big bushy pink mustache

OR

big bushy pink eyebrows?

WOULD YOU RATHER ...

be able to change colors like a chameleon

OR

hold your breath twice as long as a whale?

lose your ability to speak

OR

have to say everything you are thinking?

WOULD YOU RATHER ...

your mom never bugs you about cleaning your room again

OR

make your parents breakfast everyday?

smell terrible, but you can't smell it

OR

your parents smell terrible and you have to smell it?

WOULD YOU RATHER ...

eat poison ivy

OR

a handful of wasps?

the famous author of Twilight

OR

the famous writer of every Nickelback song?

WOULD YOU RATHER ...

wear a giant purple turtle shell on your back

OR

wear a sparkly snail shell?

never have to brush your teeth again, but have a stinky body

OR

never have to shower again, but have stinky breath?

WOULD YOU RATHER ...

know what your pets think of you

OR

never hear them speak?

be a colorful polka dotted cow

OR

a super stylish pig?

WOULD YOU RATHER ...

put your feet into a bucket of poisonous spiders

OR

put your feet in a bucket of scorpions?

laugh uncontrollably every time someone sneezes

OR

every time you yawn, someone else laughs uncontrollably?

WOULD YOU RATHER ...

go to a distant planet

OR

travel through time?

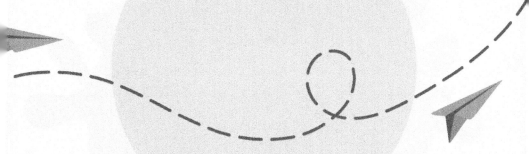

have a lavender colored eyes

OR

a purple tongue?

WOULD YOU RATHER ...

have to give a speech with a big stain on your shirt

OR

have toilet paper stuck on the bottom of both your shoes?

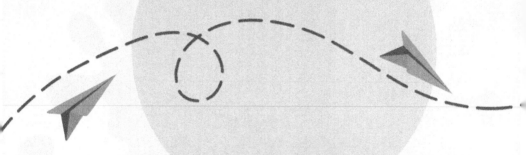

eat 50 large jars of baby food

OR

change 50 giant poopy diapers?

WOULD YOU RATHER ...

go one year without your teeth

OR

go one year without the Internet?

be a dog with human hands and legs

OR

be a human with dog paws?

WOULD YOU RATHER ...

stay awake for 41 hours straight

OR

sleep for 41 hours straight?

get pinched by a lobster ten times

OR

get punched in the face twice?

WOULD YOU RATHER ...

be a cute walking, talking avocado

OR

be a funny looking pumpkin?

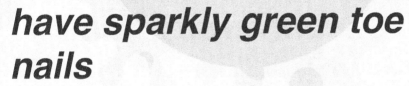

have sparkly green toe nails

OR

have sparkly green finger nails?

WOULD YOU RATHER ...

have titanium knees

OR

titanium elbows?

have a university named after you

OR

have a sports stadium named after you?

WOULD YOU RATHER ...

have all dogs try to attack you when they see you

OR

all birds try to attack you when they see you?

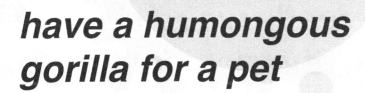

have a humongous gorilla for a pet

OR

a giant dinosaur?

WOULD YOU RATHER ...

have a car that can fly

OR

drive underwater?

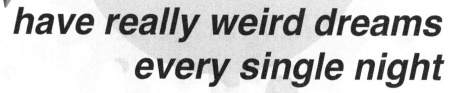

*have really weird dreams
every single night*

OR

*never have dreams ever
again?*

WOULD YOU RATHER ...

live in a place where it's always raining

OR

in a place where the sun never goes down?

have rainbow feathers for skin

OR

shiny pink scales?

WOULD YOU RATHER ...

have to eat hot soup with a fork

OR

eat frozen soup in the form of cubes?

wobble when you walk

OR

only be able to speak every other word in a sentence?

WOULD YOU RATHER ...

get famous for doing something ridiculous

OR

stay unknown your whole life?

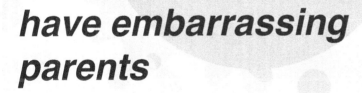

have embarrassing parents

OR

have parents who claim you embarrass them?

WOULD YOU RATHER ...

join the circus

OR

work on a farm with talking animals?

get a dollar every time someone had good thoughts about you

OR

every time someone had bad thoughts about you?

WOULD YOU RATHER ...

have pogo sticks for legs

OR

moon walk everywhere?

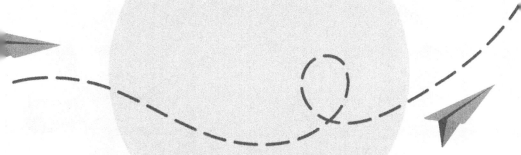

live in a spooky house with ghosts

OR

live in a house next to a cemetery?

WOULD YOU RATHER ...

that your mom reprimands every single day for a month

OR

your dad?

have legs made of jelly

OR

arms made of Cheese Wiz?

WOULD YOU RATHER ...

wear very tight underwear

OR

wear oversized underwear?

always forget your best friend's birthday

OR

your best friend always forget your birthday?

WOULD YOU RATHER ...

have a slithery tongue so long it couldn't fit into your mouth

OR

have no tongue at all?

listen to a boring speech

OR

give a really boring speech?

WOULD YOU RATHER ...

have really hairy palms

OR

really hairy fingers?

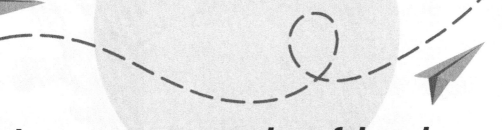

have an annoying friend who laughs too loud

OR

a friend whose laugh always sounds really fake?

WOULD YOU RATHER ...

have a slimy snail crawl up your leg

OR

crawl around in your hair?

create world peace with hugs

OR

with a massive, laughing bubble making machine?

WOULD YOU RATHER ...

scratch your butt in public

OR

sniff your butt in public?

have a friend who always begs for food

OR

have a friend who always begs for money?

WOULD YOU RATHER ...

be so hungry that you eat a meal straight out of the oven

OR

eat a meal that's gone completely frozen?

be able to talk to a baby

OR

be able to communicate with aliens light years away?

WOULD YOU RATHER ...

travel to the end of the universe

OR

discover a new species at the bottom of the ocean?

re-live the funniest day of your life every day

OR

never be able to laugh ever again?

WOULD YOU RATHER ...

be the worst at reading

OR

be a terrible writer?

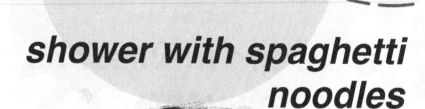

shower with spaghetti noodles

OR

shower with greasy bacon gravy?

WOULD YOU RATHER ...

live in a treehouse

OR

live in a human-sized bird nest?

have a useless superpower

OR

a superpower you don't know how to use?

WOULD YOU RATHER ...

have siblings that are nosy

OR

nosy parents?

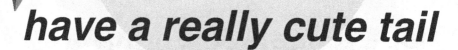

have a really cute tail

OR

really cute horns?

WOULD YOU RATHER ...

someone draw a mustache on your face while you sleep

OR

have someone paint your eyebrows while you sleep?

have hair only in the middle of your head

OR

only on the sides?

WOULD YOU RATHER ...

get a tattoo of a unicorn on your cheek

OR

a tattoo of a fairy?

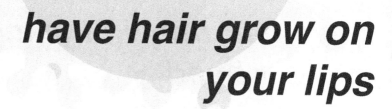

have hair grow on your lips

OR

have hair grow on your tongue?

WOULD YOU RATHER ...

eat only fruits for the rest of your life

OR

eat only junk food for the rest of your life?

have the ability to stop aging

OR

start aging faster?

WOULD YOU RATHER ...

use baby powder all over your butt

OR

all over your face?

wear a tank top outside when it's snowing really hard

OR

wear a really heavy, thick coat on a hot summer afternoon?

WOULD YOU RATHER ...

that your favorite food becomes illegal

OR

becomes very expensive to buy?

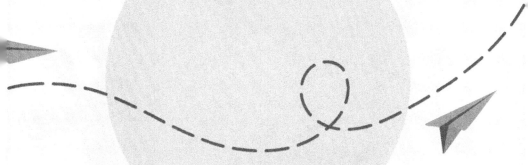

follow the same routine every day of your life

OR

perform one crazy stunt everyday?

WOULD YOU RATHER ...

have to wear wet shoes

OR

wear tight shoes?

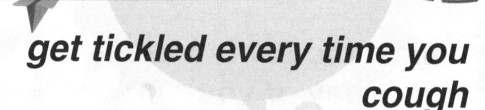

get tickled every time you cough

OR

have your arm pits get really itchy?

WOULD YOU RATHER ...

be able to see in the dark

 **OR**

have super sonic hearing?

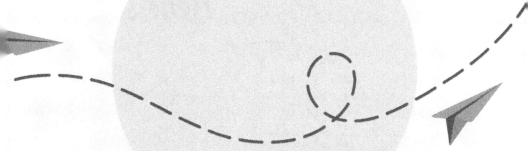

that every day is Christmas

 **OR**

your birthday?

WOULD YOU RATHER ...

walk in the rain with an umbrella that's too small

OR

with an umbrella that holes in it?

find money in your belly button

OR

a piece of candy?

WOULD YOU RATHER ...

use a friend's handkerchief to blow your nose

OR

use a friend's face towel?

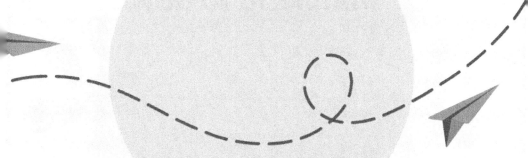

be a hilarious mummy

OR

a friendly zombie ?

WOULD YOU RATHER ...

have really long finger nails that hang down to the floor

OR

have really long eye lashes that hang to down to the floor?

have eyes on the back of your head

OR

a head that can rotate 360 degrees?

WOULD YOU RATHER ...

be able to climb walls

be able to jump from one wall to another?

control all things made of metal

control all things made of ice?

WOULD YOU RATHER ...

be stuck in a room with a cranky old man for seven days

OR

a hyper little kid?

have a bucket of cold water dumped over your head

OR

have ice blocks stuffed into your shirt?

WOULD YOU RATHER ...

wear a really itchy shirt for a whole day

OR

get stung randomly by a bee 7 times during the day?

be best friends with a skunk in a forest

OR

become best friends with a bear?

WOULD YOU RATHER ...

burp after every bite of food you eat

OR

eat a spoon full of cinnamon after every bite of food you eat?

dress up your grandparents as babies

OR

dress up your pet as an adult?

WOULD YOU RATHER ...

put lipstick on a stranger's pet

OR

have a stranger's pet put lipstick on you?

participate in a stinky cheese eating competition

OR

in a mustard drinking competition?

WOULD YOU RATHER ...

sleep in a hotel room that has a lot of bedbugs

OR

a lot of mosquitoes?

be mistaken for someone rich

OR

be mistaken for someone famous?

WOULD YOU RATHER ...

cook really delicious meals but be unable to eat them

OR

cook disgusting meals and eat them alone?

be unable to smell anything for a month

OR

not be able to taste anything for a month?

WOULD YOU RATHER ...

have claws

OR

fangs?

your mom drives you around all the time in a clown costume

OR

you drive your mom around all the time in a clown costume?

WOULD YOU RATHER ...

yell at an old lady

OR

have a young child yell at you?

ride a miniature bull

OR

a giant mosquito?

WOULD YOU RATHER ...

be stranded on an island for 74 hours

OR

be stranded on a boat for 52 hours?

be a really smart doctor

OR

be a really fun teacher?

WOULD YOU RATHER ...

go camping with talking wolves

OR

go fishing with a porcupine?

stand in a puddle of jello

OR

stand in a puddle of cream cheese?

WOULD YOU RATHER ...

cuddle a big teddy bear for 6 hours

OR

spend 3 hours cuddling with your mom?

live with your grandma

OR

live with your cousins?

WOULD YOU RATHER ...

watch cartoons

OR

dress up as cartoon characters?

find a pony on your own

OR

be surprised with a pony?

WOULD YOU RATHER ...

get good grades

OR

be really good at a sport?

help set the table for dinner

OR

help clear the table after dinner?

WOULD YOU RATHER ...

have a robot friend that makes you laugh

OR

have a robot that can do anything you ask?

have a babysitter who's really old

OR

a babysitter who's really young?

WOULD YOU RATHER ...

raise chickens

raise a herd of cows?

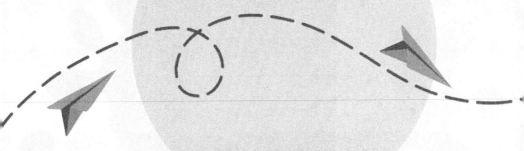

lose your favorite toy

lose all your savings?

WOULD YOU RATHER ...

have only one close friend

OR

lots of friends you're not too close to?

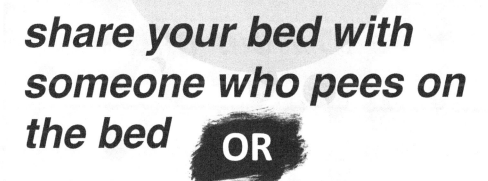

share your bed with someone who pees on the bed **OR**

one who farts a lot?

WOULD YOU RATHER ...

get presents you don't like on your birthday

OR

get no presents at all?

have to wear mittens all the time

OR

have to wear a face mask all of the time?

WOULD YOU RATHER ...

never have to go to bed again

OR

never have to wake up early?

have to dance every time you heard a song

OR

sing every time you heard a song?

WOULD YOU RATHER ...

be in a food fight

just watch a food fight
from a distance?

wake up with wings

wake up with a furry tail?

WOULD YOU RATHER ...

not have toilet paper while you're on the toilet seat

OR

not have water to wash your hands with afterward?

drink milk like a cat

OR

lick yourself like a cat?

WOULD YOU RATHER ...

have a really scary smile

 OR

have a really loud laugh?

find a cockroach
hiding in your pizza

 OR

a cockroach hiding in
your shoe?

WOULD YOU RATHER ...

have a bird make a nest in your hair

OR

a chicken lay eggs in your hair?

be able to turn yourself into a butterfly

OR

be able to turn yourself into an eagle?

WOULD YOU RATHER ...

wake up with your grandma's face

OR

wake up with your grandpa's face?

have something stuck in your teeth and not know

OR

have something dangling out of your nose and not know?

Made in the USA
Monee, IL
13 August 2020